11+ Verbal Activity

Additional Multiple-choice Practice Questions

WORKBOOK **5**

Stephen C. Curran
with Mike Edwards & Janet Peace
Edited by Andrea Richardson & Nell Bond

Accelerated Education Publications Ltd.

Contents

Chapter Eleven
LETTER SEQUENCING

The above alphabet is there to help you with these questions. Study the patterns in the sequence and write the next two letters.

Example:

AB BC CD DE EF .... Answer: **EF**

1. Level One

Exercise 11: 1 Write the next letters in the sequence.

1) **JG LI NK PM** ....

a) **RQ** b) **TO** c) **TQ** d) **SP** e) **RO**

2) **BF EI HL KO** ....

a) **QR** b) **NR** c) **PS** d) **QF** e) **NS**

3) **WY TV QS NP** ....

a) **KN** b) **JM** c) **HN** d) **KM** e) **JL**

4) **RQ PO NM LK** ....

a) **JI** b) **JJ** c) **II** d) **HJ** e) **IJ**

5) **BA DC GF IH** ....

a) **MK** b) **KJ** c) **LK** d) **KL** e) **LM**

6) **HO KR MT PW** ....

a) **SY** b) **RY** c) **QZ** d) **RZ** e) **SX**

7) **ZS WP UN RK** ....

a) **OI** b) **PJ** c) **PI** d) **PH** e) **OH**

8) **XK VI SF QD** ....

a) **NA** b) **NB** c) **OZ** d) **MB** e) **OA**

9) **AD EH IL MP** ....

a) **QT** b) **PR** c) **PT** d) **RS** e) **QS**

10) **YU TP OK JF** ....

a) **AE** b) **EA** c) **FA** d) **EB** e) **FB**

11) **WV TS PO ML** ....

a) **HG** b) **II** c) **GH** d) **GI** e) **IH**

12) **TR PN MK IG** ....

a) **ED** b) **FE** c) **FD** d) **FF** e) **EF**

13) **DE GH GH JK** ....

a) **LK** b) **LM** c) **JK** d) **JJ** e) **KJ**

14) **AI EM GO KS** ....

a) **OW** b) **NT** c) **MW** d) **MU** e) **OU**

15) **RP OM OM LJ** ....

a) **LI** b) **LJ** c) **IG** d) **GJ** e) **LG**

16) **FC IF MJ PM** ....

a) **TQ** b) **UQ** c) **TP** d) **SP** e) **SR**

17) **ZT VP SM OI** ....

a) **LF** b) **ME** c) **MF** d) **LE** e) **NE**

18) **BC BC FG FG** ....

a) **KI** b) **KF** c) **JJ** d) **JK** e) **IK**

19) **ED IH LK PO** ....

a) **RS** b) **SR** c) **TS** d) **TR** e) **SS**

20) **PL QL RJ SJ** ....

a) **UH** b) **SI** c) **TH** d) **TI** e) **SG**

Score

2. Level Two

Exercise 11: 2 Write the next letters in the sequence.

1) **FA IC LE OG** ....

a) **SJ** b) **QI** c) **RI** d) **RJ** e) **SH**

2) **BO DL FI HF** ....

a) **HH** b) **JC** c) **JE** d) **EC** e) **EH**

3) **VG XJ ZM BP** ....

a) **ER** b) **ES** c) **CR** d) **DS** e) **DT**

4) **UQ RU OY LC** ....

a) **FZ** b) **IG** c) **PZ** d) **IP** e) **PG**

5) **JA OE TJ YN** ....

a) **DS** b) **DV** c) **CS** d) **DR** e) **ES**

6) **NM HI BE VA** ....

a) **QX** b) **RW** c) **PX** d) **RV** e) **PW**

7) **WA SF OK KP** ....

a) **PU** b) **MG** c) **GL** d) **GU** e) **PL**

8) **CR XX SD NJ** ....

a) **TE** b) **IP** c) **TP** d) **JE** e) **IT**

9) **KA LB ND QG** ....

a) **UT** b) **TU** c) **UL** d) **VK** e) **UK**

10) **GG IJ JM LP** ....

a) **OR** b) **NS** c) **MS** d) **NQ** e) **MR**

11) **HE DF ZK VL RQ** ....

a) **NR** b) **OV** c) **SM** d) **NV** e) **OR**

12) **OH RL RP UT** ....

a) **UW** b) **UX** c) **WW** d) **XX** e) **XU**

13) **IK MP OU SZ** ....

a) **WE** b) **VD** c) **UE** d) **WD** e) **UB**

14) **ZU TO NJ HF BC** ....

a) **ZA** b) **VZ** c) **WZ** d) **WB** e) **VA**

15) **AZ BA DC GF KJ PO** ....

a) **VU** b) **NX** c) **VT** d) **WU** e) **UT**

16) **VE SA WW TS** ....

a) **QQ** b) **XO** c) **WP** d) **QO** e) **XP**

17) **JM IP GS DV ZY UB** ....

a) **OF** b) **PD** c) **OE** d) **QF** e) **PE**

18) **PV PO RI RD** ....

a) **TZ** b) **ZB** c) **SZ** d) **TY** e) **ZT**

19) **US WR ZP BM EI GD** ....

a) **IY** b) **JX** c) **YF** d) **JY** e) **IX**

20) **IK KP OR UW CY MD** ....

a) **WI** b) **YI** c) **WF** d) **YF** e) **WG**

Score

3. Level Three

Exercise 11: 3 Write the next letters in the sequence.

1) **BW XY GB CD LG** ....

a) **IJ** b) **GJ** c) **HG** d) **GI** e) **HI**

2) **AZ BD DU GI KP PN** ....

a) **VU** b) **UI** c) **VK** d) **UU** e) **WK**

3) **DL UI FE RZ HT** ....

a) **JN** b) **JM** c) **OO** d) **OM** e) **RN**

4) **JK YX MN UT QR QP** ....

a) **VW** b) **WX** c) **RS** d) **ML** e) **XY**

5) **ZJ BD EY IU NR** ....

a) **TQ** b) **TP** c) **SP** d) **PT** e) **SQ**

6) **PT MA SW PD VZ** ....

a) **SG** b) **VC** c) **YG** d) **YJ** e) **SC**

7) **JG SI KL RP LU QA** ....

a) **ME** b) **RH** c) **NG** d) **RE** e) **MH**

8) **FK TL JR BS VY RZ** ....

a) **NF** b) **PF** c) **FE** d) **PE** e) **ND**

9) **EG ZX LN SQ SU** ....

a) **LK** b) **JL** c) **LJ** d) **JK** e) **MK**

10) **DY GZ KB NE RI** ....

a) **UM** b) **PN** c) **UN** d) **TM** e) **TN**

Score

Chapter Twelve
ALPHABET CODES

The above alphabet is there to help you with these questions. Work out the letters that complete each question in the best way.

Example:

AB is to **BC** as **CD** is to ..DE.... Answer: **DE**

1. Level One

Exercise 12: 1 Write the letters that complete the code.

1) **JK** is to **NO** as **QH** is to ....

a) **SM** b) **UL** c) **TS** d) **SL** e) **US**

2) **DV** is to **IQ** as **SG** is to ....

a) **NB** b) **WJ** c) **NV** d) **XJ** e) **XB**

3) **NT** is to **HP** as **WE** is to ....

a) **QA** b) **BY** c) **SB** d) **SA** e) **QY**

4) **PF** is to **SL** as **MH** is to ....

a) **SK** b) **SR** c) **PK** d) **PN** e) **VN**

5) **XL** is to **XF** as **YP** is to ....

a) **ED** b) **ZJ** c) **YJ** d) **EP** e) **YP**

6) **TJ** is to **ZE** as **FN** is to ....

a) **AT** b) **LK** c) **LI** d) **KT** e) **AI**

7) **HW** is to **ET** as **SK** is to ....

a) **PN** b) **BN** c) **VH** d) **VQ** e) **PH**

8) **DU** is to **IY** as **AL** is to ....

a) **NP** b) **FQ** c) **PF** d) **FP** e) **NQ**

9) **NB** is to **HB** as **TB** is to ....

a) **NB** b) **TB** c) **NN** d) **TN** e) **BB**

10) **ZQ** is to **VM** as **PX** is to ....

a) **TT** b) **LT** c) **TX** d) **PB** e) **LB**

11) **RH** is to **XE** as **BY** is to ....

a) **YE** b) **HV** c) **VH** d) **YV** e) **HE**

12) **DN** is to **HI** as **UK** is to ....

a) **YF** b) **ZO** c) **PF** d) **PG** e) **YO**

13) **OS** is to **TM** as **NJ** is to ....

a) **SO** b) **WK** c) **SD** d) **HD** e) **HK**

14) **KV** is to **EZ** as **WG** is to ....

a) **AK** b) **QA** c) **RK** d) **QK** e) **AA**

15) **RH** is to **WM** as **DU** is to ....

a) **JZ** b) **KY** c) **IA** d) **JA** e) **IZ**

16) **EF** is to **AD** as **VX** is to ....

a) **TV** b) **RV** c) **VV** d) **RR** e) **TR**

17) **XP** is to **RJ** as **GT** is to ....

a) **AN** b) **MZ** c) **MN** d) **MA** e) **AZ**

18) **VA** is to **ZG** as **FL** is to ....

a) **JP** b) **LP** c) **LR** d) **KQ** e) **JR**

19) **MR** is to **HO** as **TP** is to ....

a) **PK** b) **QM** c) **OM** d) **QL** e) **OK**

20) **UH** is to **XD** as **AZ** is to ....

a) **DC** b) **WV** c) **EC** d) **DV** e) **WD**

Score

2. Level Two

Exercise 12: 2 Write the letters that complete the code.

1) **UY** is to **YC** as **ZD** is to ....

a) **DG** b) **ED** c) **EH** d) **DH** e) **HG**

2) **PD** is to **UY** as **XN** is to ....

a) **SS** b) **IC** c) **CS** d) **SI** e) **CI**

3) **DV** is to **XR** as **SC** is to ....

a) **MY** b) **WY** c) **MW** d) **OY** e) **OW**

4) **OX** is to **RD** as **YV** is to ....

a) **EC** b) **BB** c) **BY** d) **CY** e) **EB**

5) **LB** is to **LV** as **BC** is to ....

a) **VC** b) **CI** c) **BW** d) **VW** e) **BI**

6) **RE** is to **XZ** as **FF** is to ....

a) **LA** b) **LK** c) **ZK** d) **ZA** e) **AL**

7) **AN** is to **XJ** as **FA** is to ....

a) **BW** b) **CW** c) **IX** d) **CT** e) **BX**

8) **JC** is to **OG** as **VW** is to ....

a) **ZB** b) **AB** c) **ZA** d) **BB** e) **AA**

9) **ZZ** is to **TZ** as **AA** is to ....

a) **UT** b) **ZT** c) **GA** d) **UA** e) **GZ**

10) **DV** is to **ZR** as **WB** is to ....

a) **AX** b) **XA** c) **SX** d) **AF** e) **SF**

11) **UC** is to **AZ** as **YA** is to ....

a) **EX** b) **ED** c) **SG** d) **VX** e) **SD**

12) **LD** is to **PY** as **XF** is to ....

a) **UJ** b) **BA** c) **TB** d) **BJ** e) **TA**

13) **HE** is to **MY** as **ZS** is to ....

a) **EX** b) **UM** c) **TS** d) **EM** e) **UX**

14) **JN** is to **DR** as **FW** is to ....

a) **ZS** b) **JS** c) **ZA** d) **LQ** e) **LA**

15) **AY** is to **FD** as **XB** is to ....

a) **CW** b) **GW** c) **SG** d) **SC** e) **CG**

16) **CQ** is to **YO** as **UA** is to ....

a) **QU** b) **RA** c) **QY** d) **SY** e) **SA**

17) **EP** is to **YJ** as **BR** is to ....

a) **VL** b) **BX** c) **HR** d) **VX** e) **HL**

18) **NV** is to **RB** as **YZ** is to ....

a) **CD** b) **ET** c) **UD** d) **EF** e) **CF**

19) **OC** is to **JZ** as **CX** is to ....

a) **HA** b) **ZU** c) **HS** d) **XS** e) **XU**

20) **FG** is to **IC** as **ZB** is to ....

a) **WF** b) **CX** c) **VX** d) **WE** e) **CE**

Score

3. Level Three

Exercise 12: 3 Write the letters that complete the code.

1) **XY** is to **BC** as **WZ** is to ....

a) **AD** b) **AV** c) **SG** d) **FV** e) **SD**

2) **VC** is to **AX** as **ZD** is to ....

a) **HI** b) **UY** c) **EU** d) **UI** e) **EY**

3) **AC** is to **UY** as **DB** is to ....

a) **JF** b) **XJ** c) **JJ** d) **XX** e) **ZX**

4) **YU** is to **BA** as **XW** is to ....

a) **QZ** b) **AC** c) **UQ** d) **AZ** e) **UC**

5) **AD** is to **ZW** as **BE** is to ....

a) **XV** b) **YV** c) **YW** d) **AW** e) **AY**

6) **XZ** is to **FS** as **UC** is to ....

a) **VC** b) **BW** c) **UB** d) **DV** e) **CV**

7) **EI** is to **VR** as **JU** is to ....

a) **QF** b) **PE** c) **QE** d) **FQ** e) **RF**

8) **CF** is to **TM** as **AW** is to ....

a) **DR** b) **DS** c) **SE** d) **RD** e) **RE**

9) **HS** is to **SH** as **TK** is to ....

a) **GT** b) **GK** c) **TP** d) **GP** e) **KP**

10) **GR** is to **TI** as **QE** is to ....

a) **JV** b) **VW** c) **VJ** d) **WV** e) **JW**

Score

A B C D E F G H I J K L M N O P Q R S T U V W X Y Z

Chapter Thirteen

MORE ALPHABET CODES

The above alphabet is there to help you with these questions. Each question has a different code. Work out the correct answer by using the code provided.

Example:

The code for **BABY** is **CBCZ**.

Work out the code for **FOAL**. GPBM

1. Level One

Exercise 13: 1 Work out the code for the given word.

Score

1) The code for **GNAT** is **HOBU**.
Work out the code for **HELP**. ....

a) **IMQF** b) **FIMQ** c) **IFMP** d) **IFMQ** e) **IFMR**

2) The code for **KITE** is **IGRC**.
Work out the code for **LOST**. ....

a) **JMQR** b) **MJQR** c) **JMQT** d) **RJMQ** e) **JMQV**

3) The code for **MATE** is **PDWH**.
Work out the code for **EDGE**. ....

a) **GHHJ** b) **HHGJ** c) **HGJH** d) **HGJE** e) **EGJH**

4) The code for **POND** is **MLKA**.
Work out the code for **NEWS**. ....

a) **PKBT** b) **KBTS** c) **KBWP** d) **NBTP** e) **KBTP**

5) The code for **RIPE** is **PGNC**.
Work out the code for **POST**. ....

a) **NMQT** b) **NMRQ** c) **MNQR** d) **NMQR** e) **PMQR**

6) The code for **SINK** is **RHMJ**.
Work out the code for **RIDE**. ....

a) **QCDH** b) **QHCD** c) **HQCD** d) **QHCE** e) **RHCE**

7) The code for **OVER** is **RYHU**.
Work out the code for **MILK**. ....

a) **PLON** b) **LPON** c) **MLON** d) **NOLP** e) **PLOK**

8) The code for **LIME** is **NKOG**.
Work out the code for **HAIR**. ....

a) **CKTT** b) **JAKT** c) **JCKT** d) **JCKR** e) **TJKC**

9) The code for **HYMN** is **EVJK**.
Work out the code for **GULP**. ....

a) **GRIS** b) **DRLM** c) **DRMI** d) **RDIM** e) **DRIM**

10) The code for **LEAP** is **MFBQ**.
Work out the code for **FILM**. ....

a) **JGMN** b) **GJMN** c) **GIMN** d) **NMJG** e) **FJMN**

11) The code for **DUMP** is **BSKN**.
Work out the code for **CREW**. ....

a) **APCU** b) **APCW** c) **UCPA** d) **CUAP** e) **ACPU**

12) The code for **BOAR** is **ERDU**.
Work out the code for **ANTS**. ....

a) **DVWQ** b) **AQWV** c) **DQWV** d) **DQWU** e) **DWVQ**

13) The code for **SAVE** is **UCXG**.
Work out the code for **JOIN**. ....

a) **PKQL** b) **LKQP** c) **JQKP** d) **LQKP** e) **KPLQ**

14) The code for **GOWN** is **FNVM**.
Work out the code for **WIND**. ....

a) **VHMC** b) **CMHV** c) **VCMH** d) **HVMC** e) **VIMC**

15) The code for **WEST** is **TBPQ**.
Work out the code for **KING**. ....

a) **FHKD** b) **HDKF** c) **HFKD** d) **KDHF** e) **HFKH**

16) The code for **LAWN** is **MBXO**.
Work out the code for **HOLE**. ....

a) **FMPI** b) **IMPF** c) **MFIP** d) **IPME** e) **IPMF**

17) The code for **WINK** is **UGLI**.
Work out the code for **TURN**. ....

a) **LPSR** b) **RSPN** c) **PRSL** d) **RSPL** e) **RSPR**

18) The code for **SWIM** is **VZLP**.
Work out the code for **RAIL**. ....

a) **ODLU** b) **UDLO** c) **UDOL** d) **UDLL** e) **DLOU**

19) The code for **VERB** is **UDQA**.
Work out the code for **WINE**. ....

a) **VHMD** b) **VDMH** c) **VHME** d) **VHMV** e) **HMDV**

20) The code for **TUBE** is **VWDG**.
Work out the code for **RASH**. ....

a) **TDVJ** b) **CTUJ** c) **TCUJ** d) **UJTC** e) **TCUK**

2. Level Two

Exercise 13: 2 Work out the code or word.

Score

1) The code for **CLUMP** is **FOXPS**.
Work out the code for **DRAFT**. ....

a) **WIDUG** b) **GUDWI** c) **GUWDI** d) **IGUDW** e) **GUDIW**

2) The code for **FOAMY** is **HQCOA**.
What is the word for **INCBG**? ....

a) **GLASS** b) **GLAZE** c) **BLAZE** d) **GLOVE** e) **GLUED**

3) The code for **ENJOY** is **DMINX**.
Work out the code for **HUMAN**. ....

a) **GTLZM** b) **TGLZM** c) **MZLTG** d) **GMLTZ** e) **GTLMZ**

4) The code for **GROAN** is **KVSER**.
What is the word for **MQEKI**? ....

a) **IMPEL** b) **INERT** c) **IMAGE** d) **INNER** e) **IONIC**

5) The code for **LUCKY** is **JSAIW**.
Work out the code for **MELON**. ....

a) **KCJLM** b) **LMJCK** c) **KLCJM** d) **KCJML** e) **MKCLJ**

6) The code for **PLATE** is **OKZSD**.
What is the word for **MTQRD**? ....

a) **NURSE** b) **NOISE** c) **NUDGE** d) **NYLON** e) **WORTH**

7) The code for **OLDER** is **ROGHU**.
Work out the code for **TEARS**. ....

a) **HWDUV** b) **WDHUV** c) **WHDUV** d) **VWHDU** e) **WHDVU**

8) The code for **SCRAP** is **OYNWL**.
What is the word for **NWZEK**? ....

a) **RAPID** b) **RANGE** c) **RADAR** d) **ANGEL** e) **RADIO**

9) The code for **THROB** is **WKURE**.
Work out the code for **VEILS**. ....

a) **VOLHY** b) **YHLOV** c) **YLHOV** d) **LYHVO** e) **YHLVO**

10) The code for **WALTZ** is **XBMUA**.
What is the word for **FYUSB**? ....

a) **EXTRA** b) **ENTER** c) **EXERT** d) **EXIST** e) **ERECT**

11) The code for **FRONT** is **BNKJP**.
Work out the code for **DICED**. ....

a) **ZZEYA** b) **EYAZZ** c) **ZEYAZ** d) **ZEYZA** e) **YAZEZ**

12) The code for **COAST** is **EQCUV**.
Work out the code for **HONEY**. ....

a) **AGPQJ** b) **JQPAG** c) **PQJAG** d) **GJQPA** e) **JQPGA**

13) The code for **DECAY** is **HIGEC**.
What is the word for **ASVWI**? ....

a) **WOODS** b) **WORSE** c) **SORRY** d) **WORST** e) **WAIST**

14) The code for **CLIMB** is **ZIFJY**.
What is the word for **AXRKQ**? ....

a) **DAUNT** b) **DOUBT** c) **STING** d) **DAIRY** e) **DRAIN**

15) The code for **ISLES** is **KTNFU**.
Work out the code for **PLEAT**. ....

a) **RNFBV** b) **RMNCV** c) **RMGBV** d) **RMGCV** e) **GNRCV**

16) The code for **WEARY** is **BJFWD**.
Work out the code for **VIXEN**. ....

a) **NACJS** b) **ANCJS** c) **ACNJS** d) **AJNSC** e) **JANCS**

17) The code for **ENGAGE** is **ZIBVBZ**.
What is the word for **WDNCJK**? ....

a) **INSECT** b) **BISQUE** c) **BISHOP** d) **WISHES** e) **BASINS**

18) The code for **EARTH** is **AWNPD**.
What is the word for **BHKWP**? ....

a) **RAISE** b) **FLAME** c) **FLOAT** d) **FLOWN** e) **FLORA**

19) The code for **LOCATE** is **QTHFYJ**.
What is the word for **XHTWJI**? ....

a) **SCORED** b) **SCORER** c) **SCORES**
d) **SCORCH** e) **SOCCER**

20) The code for **UPWARD** is **XSZDUG**.
What is the word for **WUXVWB**? ....

a) **TRUSTY** b) **TRUNKS** c) **GRUDGE**
d) **TRUANT** e) **TRUDGE**

3. Level Three

Exercise 13: 3 Work out the code or word.

1) The code for **FROWN** is **EPLSI**.
Work out the code for **EJECT**. ....

a) **IHAXO** b) **DIBYO** c) **DHBYM** d) **DIDBS** e) **DHBYO**

2) The code for **CHOSEN** is **DJPUFP**.
Work out the code for **BREACH**. ....

a) **CTFCDJ** b) **TCFCDJ** c) **CTFCJD**
d) **DEJTGC** e) **CDGTEJ**

3) The code for **GAUZE** is **JXXWH**.
What is the word for **IOXFW**? ....

a) **FRUIT** b) **TRAIN** c) **FRIED** d) **GROWN** e) **FRUMP**

4) The code for **ASCENT** is **ZUBGMV**.
Work out the code for **ABIDES**. ....

a) **ZHFBDU** b) **UFZHBD** c) **ZFBHDU**
d) **BHZDZU** e) **ZDHFDU**

5) The code for **ELATED** is **VOZGVW**.
Work out the code for **DIVINE**. ....

a) **WERMRV** b) **WRERMV** c) **VMRERW**
d) **WRERVM** e) **RMRVEW**

6) The code for **CYCLE** is **AVYGY**.
Work out the code for **DOVES**. ....

a) **BMSZM** b) **BLSZM** c) **BMTQC** d) **QMCBT** e) **BLRZM**

7) The code for **RUSTIC** is **PQQPGY**.
Work out the code for **SEATED**. ....

a) **QBYPCZ** b) **QAYPCZ** c) **QAPCZC**
d) **WQCRAB** e) **QAYPCY**

8) The code for **SALMON** is **HZONLM**.
What is the word for **IVDZIW**? ....

a) **WINDOW** b) **REWIRE** c) **WORLDS**
d) **REWARD** e) **REVOLT**

9) The code for **BRIAR** is **CTLEW**.
What is the word for **BYIYQ**? ....

a) **AWARE** b) **AUDIT** c) **AWARD** d) **AWFUL** e) **WARES**

10) The code for **WORK** is **DLIP**.
Work out the code for **CIRCUS**. ....

a) **XRXIFH** b) **HFXIRX** c) **XRIXFH**
d) **XHRIXF** e) **IXFHXR**

Score

Chapter Fourteen

ONE WORD PATTERNS

In these questions there are three pairs of words. The last pair of words is made up in the **same way** as the first two pairs. Work out the missing word.

Example:

Find the missing word:

(sand and) (said aid)
(sink ?) ......ink......

1. Level One

Exercise 14: 1 Work out the missing word.

1) **(depot top) (straw war)**
(bonus ?) ....

a) **son** b) **pot** c) **sun** d) **sob** e) **raw**

2) **(chart tar) (aware ear)**
(brawl ?) ....

a) **raw** b) **law** c) **lab** d) **hat** e) **are**

3) **(caper pea) (deter tee)**
(chase ?) ....

a) **ace** b) **ape** c) **sea** d) **ash** e) **sap**

4) **(grabs bar) (newel ewe)**
(crack ?) ....

a) **bag** b) **rag** c) **cab** d) **web** e) **car**

5) **(pitch hit) (songs son)**
(pined ?) ....

a) **pin** b) **die** c) **din** d) **pie** e) **den**

6) **(glared are) (floret ore)**
(crater ?) ....

a) **are** b) **ate** c) **arc** d) **car** e) **cat**

7) **(gunner rug) (sallow was)**
(gambit ?) ....

a) **bag** b) **mat** c) **tag** d) **bat** e) **big**

8) **(riddle lid) (tapers rap)**
(vanity ?) ....

a) **tin** b) **nit** c) **van** d) **nay** e) **tan**

9) **(ushers her) (voting tin)**
(uptown ?) ....

a) **top** b) **ton** c) **not** d) **tow** e) **won**

10) **(trader rat) (shamed has)**
(tarsal ?) ....

a) **tar** b) **art** c) **eat** d) **ate** e) **tea**

11) **(awfully full) (besides side)**
(washing ?) ....

a) **hash** b) **sing** c) **shin** d) **sang** e) **gain**

12) **(instead tins) (oilskin soil)**

(rapture ?) ....

a) **part** b) **tare** c) **reap** d) **trip** e) **trap**

13) **(furtive turf) (prattle trap)**

(droplet ?) ....

a) **prod** b) **rope** c) **pelt** d) **lord** e) **dope**

14) **(warship wash) (melanin mean)**

(calmest ?) ....

a) **case** b) **same** c) **late** d) **came** e) **calm**

15) **(armhole mole) (casting sing)**

(astride ?) ....

a) **diet** b) **tide** c) **ride** d) **tier** e) **tire**

16) **(stones note) (martyr tray)**

(stared ?) ....

a) **rats** b) **star** c) **tsar** d) **rate** e) **rare**

17) **(dashing sing) (cornice rice)**

(emptied ?) ....

a) **pint** b) **time** c) **pain** d) **ripe** e) **pied**

18) **(profile life) (salvage gave)**

(realist ?) ....

a) **tear** b) **sits** c) **silt** d) **sear** e) **slit**

19) **(bangles base) (windier wire)**
(hairier ?) ....

a) **hair** b) **hire** c) **hide** d) **hare** e) **hard**

20) **(grouped pour) (starter tart)**
(greater ?) ....

a) **teat** b) **rate** c) **tare** d) **rear** e) **tear**

Score

2. Level Two

Exercise 14: 2 Work out the missing word.

1) **(attacks tack) (easiest sees)**
(affirms ?) ....

a) **firm** b) **farm** c) **fame** d) **fair** e) **firs**

2) **(endless sled) (sheikhs hike)**
(enthuse ?) ....

a) **sent** b) **shut** c) **suet** d) **hunt** e) **hens**

3) **(muddier dime) (puppies pipe)**
(rescued ?) ....

a) **sued** b) **sure** c) **cued** d) **suds** e) **code**

4) **(lanolin loin) (expanse ease)**
(several ?) ....

a) **seep** b) **rave** c) **seal** d) **veer** e) **seen**

5) **(mariner rain) (relates seat)**
(connect ?) ....

a) **tons** b) **sons** c) **toes** d) **real** e) **tone**

6) **(pothole pool) (tombola tool)**
(through ?) ....

a) **thou** b) **oath** c) **tore** d) **thug** e) **tare**

7) **(learner near) (hearten tear)**
(overeat ?) ....

a) **ever** b) **rove** c) **even** d) **rate** e) **over**

8) **(imperil limp) (ledgers sled)**
(untruth ?) ....

a) **huts** b) **runt** c) **turn** d) **hurt** e) **hunt**

9) **(spotted dote) (turning grin)**
(nowhere ?) ....

a) **were** b) **ever** c) **ewer** d) **went** e) **here**

10) **(snooker rook) (coastal last)**
(trailer ?) ....

a) **rate** b) **tear** c) **rare** d) **rail** e) **tail**

11) **(farmers rare) (fillets tile)**
(healthy ?) ....

a) **heat** b) **than** c) **heal** d) **teal** e) **heel**

12) **(forester rest) (numbered deer)**
(patented ?) ....

a) **tent** b) **tape** c) **pant** d) **dent** e) **deep**

13) **(honoured node) (mirrored ride)**
(rampager ?) ....

a) **rear** b) **mead** c) **mane** d) **main** e) **mare**

14) **(assembly less) (treasure rare)**
(careless ?) ....

a) **team** b) **sear** c) **seat** d) **sale** e) **seas**

15) **(stresses rest) (esteemed tees)**
(numeracy ?) ....

a) **mean** b) **menu** c) **race** d) **year** e) **care**

16) **(tuneless nest) (solstice lies)**
(debonair ?) ....

a) **barn** b) **dare** c) **band** d) **bard** e) **dear**

17) **(archway wary) (incense nine)**
(inaptly ?) ....

a) **tint** b) **pant** c) **tiny** d) **pint** e) **tile**

18) **(employed yelp) (canoeing icon)**
(mutineer ?) ....

a) **time** b) **elms** c) **emit** d) **tune** e) **mute**

19) **(advanced dead) (sensible else)**
(radiance ?) ....

a) **acid** b) **area** c) **dice** d) **acre** e) **raid**

20) **(escapade pace) (fearless leaf)**
(diastole ?) ....

a) **toes** b) **sole** c) **tile** d) **toad** e) **sail**

Score

3. Level Three

Exercise 14: 3 Work out the missing word.

1) **(peppers peep) (lattice tail)**
(message ?) ....

a) **game** b) **seam** c) **same** d) **ages** e) **sage**

2) **(laggard gaga) (resents seen)**
(homonym ?) ....

a) **soon** b) **many** c) **home** d) **moon** e) **most**

3) **(retorted tree) (outdoors tour)**
(casework ?) ....

a) **scar** b) **weak** c) **cars** d) **soar** e) **soak**

4) **(berserk beer) (condole cool)**
(herself ?) ....

a) **hers** b) **seal** c) **heel** d) **safe** e) **heal**

5) **(gallant gala) (decried dice)**
(pension ?) ....

a) **pies** b) **spin** c) **nose** d) **pine** e) **pins**

6) **(defence feed) (ratline tear)**
(deserve ?) ....

a) **seal** b) **teal** c) **deed** d) **sear** e) **seed**

7) **(purebred reed) (embalmer bear)**
(balanced ?) ....

a) **dale** b) **need** c) **land** d) **leap** e) **lead**

8) **(creepers peer) (idealist lied)**
(grandeur ?) ....

a) **darn** b) **dear** c) **rand** d) **rude** e) **dean**

9) **(arrested rare) (weediest ewes)**
(includes ?) ....

a) **clue** b) **iced** c) **nice** d) **sine** e) **nude**

10) **(niftiest fist) (saltiest last)**
(forebear ?) ....

a) **robe** b) **bear** c) **fore** d) **rear** e) **roar**

Score

Chapter Fifteen
TWO WORD PATTERNS

In these questions, the word in the middle of the second group is made in the **same way** as the word in the middle of the first group. Fill in the word that is missing in the second group.

Example:

Fill in the missing word:

(sea [set] top) (pen [......pet......] too)

1. Level One

Exercise 15: 1 Fill in the missing word.

1) **(teak [soak] sort) (fish [......................] pole)**

   a) **ship** b) **shop** c) **posh** d) **pose** e) **hole**

2) **(port [thou] huge) (grub [......................] year)**

   a) **byre** b) **bray** c) **rear** d) **rare** e) **bear**

3) **(foam [tame] type) (heat [......................] push)**

   a) **pate** b) **shut** c) **huts** d) **pest** e) **path**

4) **(colt [calf] fray) (limp [......................] bear)**

   a) **bare** b) **lamb** c) **lame** d) **lamp** e) **pail**

5) **(rope [soap] task) (ripe [......................] isle)**

   a) **less** b) **list** c) **pile** d) **lisp** e) **pier**

6) **(hump [camp] cola) (bold [.....................] hide)**

a) **hold** b) **bile** c) **bide** d) **held** e) **lied**

7) **(wick [chew] shoe) (lush [.....................] sari)**

a) **rush** b) **sail** c) **hail** d) **wish** e) **rash**

8) **(fray [tear] dote) (home [.....................] time)**

a) **mite** b) **meet** c) **memo** d) **time** e) **emit**

9) **(mead [shed] hops) (sign [.....................] ever)**

a) **give** b) **seen** c) **revs** d) **sing** e) **rein**

10) **(whim [much] cute) (stag [.....................] limp)**

a) **gist** b) **slap** c) **slip** d) **pail** e) **gilt**

11) **(fate [fuel] luck) (turn [.....................] aunt)**

a) **taut** b) **runt** c) **tuna** d) **tarn** e) **rant**

12) **(twin [news] sloe) (arch [.....................] once)**

a) **hero** b) **cone** c) **hare** d) **hear** e) **care**

13) **(malt [real] bore) (stow [.....................] cave)**

a) **vote** b) **veto** c) **vast** d) **vest** e) **stew**

14) **(waft [part] spur) (barn [.....................] flow)**

a) **loan** b) **blow** c) **warn** d) **lawn** e) **flan**

15) **(holy [heal] cage) (lath [.....................] ante)**

a) **lean** b) **than** c) **heat** d) **lent** e) **late**

16) **(glad [drug] rush) (dray [.....................] area)**

a) **year** b) **read** c) **dear** d) **dare** e) **yard**

17) **(mute [rude] bird) (mine [.....................] film)**

a) **lime** b) **line** c) **mile** d) **file** e) **life**

18) **(gate [tray] byre) (duty [.....................] from)**

a) **tofu** b) **tour** c) **trod** d) **dram** e) **your**

19) **(puma [peat] kite) (saga [.....................] harp)**

a) **gasp** b) **rasp** c) **spar** d) **hash** e) **sear**

20) **(lane [gone] yoga) (wash [.....................] dupe)**

a) **shed** b) **paws** c) **push** d) **swap** e) **dash**

Score

2. Level Two

Exercise 15: 2 Fill in the missing word.

1) **(wrest [core] porch) (parch [.....................] stash)**

a) **star** b) **rash** c) **sash** d) **part** e) **hart**

2) **(doubt [grub] barge) (charm [.....................] waste)**

a) **tram** b) **warm** c) **stem** d) **team** e) **tsar**

3) **(joule [coal] camel) (dolly [..................] since)**

a) **sold** b) **soul** c) **slid** d) **soil** e) **dole**

4) **(power [wane] fauna) (speed [..................] sleep)**

a) **deep** b) **epee** c) **peep** d) **epic** e) **seed**

5) **(dream [name] plain) (notes [..................] sheep)**

a) **then** b) **pest** c) **pets** d) **pots** e) **stop**

6) **(point [mist] music) (aloud [..................] worse)**

a) **word** b) **lord** c) **ruse** d) **wore** e) **rude**

7) **(seize [deer] rigid) (scuba [..................] names)**

a) **scam** b) **numb** c) **scab** d) **scan** e) **mean**

8) **(amend [dine] image) (blunt [..................] exist)**

a) **tens** b) **sent** c) **test** d) **text** e) **tent**

9) **(carve [race] piper) (least [..................] tools)**

a) **aims** b) **last** c) **sell** d) **sets** e) **toss**

10) **(cabin [coal] igloo) (pause [..................] mayor)**

a) **prey** b) **pure** c) **pray** d) **seam** e) **your**

11) **(lilac [goal] ingot) (exert [..................] music)**

a) **must** b) **site** c) **rise** d) **sire** e) **mute**

12) **(girth [rich] scree) (point [....................] cameo)**

a) **into** b) **tone** c) **mope** d) **pint** e) **moat**

13) **(irony [rent] mitre) (lunge [....................] spear)**

a) **urns** b) **urge** c) **pear** d) **ants** e) **spun**

14) **(tawny [lane] valet) (windy [....................] cater)**

a) **tide** b) **tire** c) **cart** d) **wine** e) **tape**

15) **(spade [caps] piece) (bride [....................] mould)**

a) **limb** b) **ride** c) **dire** d) **lied** e) **mild**

16) **(vague [gust] taste) (track [....................] cares)**

a) **aces** b) **rack** c) **cart** d) **arts** e) **acre**

17) **(avail [gilt] giant) (habit [....................] pansy)**

a) **pint** b) **than** c) **pans** d) **pity** e) **snap**

18) **(guess [edge] horde) (laird [....................] slide)**

a) **lids** b) **idle** c) **isle** d) **idea** e) **ends**

19) **(canoe [face] mafia) (faint [....................] bosun)**

a) **snob** b) **snub** c) **soft** d) **buns** e) **sofa**

20) **(bulky [blue] cruet) (train [....................] tenth)**

a) **tart** b) **tarn** c) **hart** d) **tent** e) **rent**

Score

3. Level Three

Exercise 15: 3 Fill in the missing word.

1) **(start [roast] arrow)** **(novel [..................] aspic)**
   a) **piano** b) **spice** c) **spine** d) **pines** e) **clasp**

2) **(funny [fund] fudge)** **(prove [..................] forge)**
   a) **pore** b) **poor** c) **rove** d) **gore** e) **fore**

3) **(algae [legal] eagle)** **(sense [..................] white)**
   a) **tenth** b) **whist** c) **tense** d) **heist** e) **tents**

4) **(treat [rate] tear)** **(scoot [..................] axle)**
   a) **coal** b) **coat** c) **lest** d) **coax** e) **lost**

5) **(penne [open] pond)** **(where [..................] cart)**
   a) **care** b) **race** c) **ware** d) **aces** e) **ache**

6) **(theme [dame] madam)** **(preen [..................] grove)**
   a) **ripe** b) **open** c) **oven** d) **ogre** e) **vent**

7) **(islet [sleet] tiles)** **(spoil [..................] thing)**
   a) **toils** b) **pints** c) **loins** d) **sting** e) **point**

8) **(tower [ewer] fares)** **(shown [..................] shirt)**
   a) **wart** b) **wean** c) **woes** d) **wont** e) **worn**

9) **(level [reel] lever)** **(lunge [..................] autos)**
   a) **soul** b) **song** c) **tuna** d) **sage** e) **solo**

10) **(deed [bode] blob)** **(rhea [..................] burn)**
   a) **hear** b) **bulb** c) **brag** d) **bear** e) **brae**

Score

Chapter Sixteen
SECRET CODES

In these questions there are four words. Three of the words have been given a code. The codes are not written in the same order as the words. Work out the code for the given word.

Example:

PAL LAP PEA APE

421 413 314

Work out the code for **EEL**. ......223......

1. Level One

Exercise 16: 1 Work out the code.

Score

SEAS EASE SONS SEEN

4124 2412 2445

1) Work out the code for **SANE**. ....

a) **2514** b) **2152** c) **2154** d) **4512** e) **5124**

2) Work out the code for **SOON**. ....

a) **2352** b) **2355** c) **2332** d) **2335** e) **2325**

3) Work out the code for **SEASONS**. ....

a) **2142325** b) **2412532** c) **1425231** d) **2213452** e) **2412352**

HEAT DEAR READ TEAR

3615 5613 2613

4) Work out the code for **DATE**. ....

a) **5612** b) **5146** c) **5216** d) **5126** e) **1456**

5) Work out the code for **THERE**. ....

a) **24536** b) **23636** c) **51263** d) **24565** e) **24636**

6) Work out the code for **DARED**. ....

a) **61356** b) **51365** c) **51325** d) **51635** e) **54365**

TOES RODE TROD REST

4562 2356 4315

7) Work out the code for **TEST**. ....

a) **2652** b) **5265** c) **2562** d) **2256** e) **6522**

8) Work out the code for **STRODE**. ....

a) **263415** b) **624315** c) **624513** d) **513264** e) **641253**

9) Work out the code for **SORTED**. ....

a) **643125** b) **634215** c) **631254** d) **634512** e) **634251**

LINE BEND DINE LIED

3712 5617 2617

10) Work out the code for **IDLE**. ....

a) **2672** b) **5612** c) **6527** d) **6257** e) **6275**

11) Work out the code for **KINDLE**. ....

a) **461257** b) **461527** c) **416275** d) **614257** e) **571462**

12) Work out the code for **BLINKED**. ....

a) **3561742** b) **5364712** c) **3514762** d) **5634127** e) **3561472**

BEAD TOAD DOTE BOAT

3412 3716 2416

13) Work out the code for **DEBT**. ....

a) **2136** b) **6732** c) **6723** d) **6742** e) **7132**

14) Work out the code for **TABLE**. ....

a) **23157** b) **21357** c) **21356** d) **57312** e) **21537**

15) Work out the code for **BLOATED**. ....

a) **3451276** b) **3215467** c) **541237** d) **3541276** e) **6721435**

BAKE CART RACE TACK

3561 7514 6523

16) Work out the code for **BEAT**. ....

a) **7451** b) **6453** c) **7653** d) **7453** e) **6543**

17) Work out the code for **CRATE**. ....

a) **65234** b) **35264** c) **62354** d) **54362** e) **62534**

18) Work out the code for **BRACKET**. ....

a) **7526143** b) **7256134** c) **7256143** d) **7256413** e) **7653412**

RAGE REAR GEAR GRAN

3542 2435 2542

19) Work out the code for **RANG**. ....

a) **3124** b) **2413** c) **2431** d) **4213** e) **2314**

20) Work out the code for **ANGER**. ....

a) **46352** b) **13254** c) **41352** d) **41235** e) **31252**

2. Level Two

Exercise 16: 2 Write the word or code.

Score

RASH SHED HEAR AREA
6251 2573 3762

1) Work out the code for **REAR**. ....

a) **7357** b) **3753** c) **3575** d) **3573** e) **5375**

2) What is the word for **62735**? ....

a) **SHEAR** b) **HEARS** c) **SHARE** d) **HEARD** e) **SHEDS**

3) Work out the code for **CRASHED**. ....

a) **4736251** b) **4376251** c) **3476152** d) **4376521** e) **3746215**

BLED ABLE BEAN BALE
5123 5241 5416

4) Work out the code for **LEAD**. ....

a) **4261** b) **4162** c) **5416** d) **2146** e) **4126**

5) What is the word for **54261**? ....

a) **BLADE** b) **SHADE** c) **BEARD** d) **BLARE** e) **BARED**

6) Work out the code for **ENABLED**. ....

a) **1324516** b) **1574613** c) **1654713** d) **1325416** e) **1235416**

POLE MILE COPE LIME
4561 6541 3741

7) Work out the code for **PILE**. ....

a) **3514** b) **5431** c) **3541** d) **3451** e) **5341**

8) What is the word for **3741652**? ....

a) **COPPICE** b) **POLEMIC** c) **COMPILE**
d) **POLECAT** e) **PICCOLO**

9) Work out the code for **PEOPLES**. ....

a) **3174137** b) **1373418** c) **3173418** d) **3713418** e) **3174318**

TEST EAST RENT NEAR
4321 5365 1345

10) Work out the code for **STAR**. ....

a) **5614** b) **6512** c) **6521** d) **5621** e) **6125**

11) What is the word for **53263**? ....

a) **TEAMS** b) **STERN** c) **TREAT** d) **SEATS** e) **TEASE**

12) Work out the code for **EASTERN**. ....

a) **3265134** b) **3265314** c) **3263524** d) **2365341** e) **6325143**

TEAL HALE WELT LATE
2167 5716 3765

13) Work out the code for **TALE**. ....

a) **5167** b) **5176** c) **6157** d) **5671** e) **6571**

14) What is the word for **32776**? ....

a) **TALLY** b) **WHEAL** c) **LATTE**
d) **WHEEL** e) **WHEAT**

15) Work out the code for **WEALTHY**. ....

a) **3176524** b) **3715624** c) **7316542**
d) **4716524** e) **3716524**

MATE JEST STAY TEAM

7615 1523 4256

16) Work out the code for **MAST**. ....

a) **6215** b) **4215** c) **6521** d) **4521** e) **4251**

17) What is the word for **156243**? ....

a) **STATES** b) **TASTES** c) **STEAMY**
d) **ESTEEM** e) **STEELS**

18) Work out the code for **MAJESTY**. ....

a) **2476125** b) **4276513** c) **4271653**
d) **4276153** e) **4726153**

DEAD TAUT NEAT AUNT

7154 3153 4564

19) Work out the code for **NEED**. ....

a) **3117** b) **1773** c) **3711** d) **7331** e) **7113**

20) Work out the code for **DAUNTED**. ....

a) **3567413** b) **3567143** c) **3561374**
d) **5367435** e) **3567314**

3. Level Three

Exercise 16: 3 Write the word or code.

Score

CARE REAP LACE SEAL

7236 3216 4627

1) Work out the code for **EASE**. ....

a) **3243** b) **6426** c) **6246** d) **7247** e) **6242**

2) What is the word for **1676246**? ....

a) **RESEALS** b) **SCRAPES** c) **REPEALS**
d) **RELEASE** e) **PLEASES**

3) Work out the code for **PARCELS.** ....

a) **3647512** b) **5123647** c) **5213764**
d) **5213674** e) **5214674**

MEAD READ MARE RARE

5412 1243 1412

4) Work out the code for **MADE.** ....

a) **5342** b) **5423** c) **2325** d) **4325** e) **5432**

5) What is the word for **124321**? ....

a) **REDEEM** b) **MARRED** c) **READER**
d) **REMADE** e) **MADDER**

6) Work out the code for **DREAMERS.** ....

a) **62135124** b) **31254216** c) **31245126**
d) **31245216** e) **32145216**

CARE EATS CASH RATE

7254 7231 3261

7) Work out the code for **SEAR.** ....

a) **5132** b) **5123** c) **3251** d) **5423** e) **1523**

8) What is the word for **412613**? ....

a) **SHARES** b) **HEATER** c) **ARCHES**
d) **HATTER** e) **CHEERS**

9) Work out the code for **TEACHERS.** ....

a) **51734135** b) **61374136** c) **61274315**
d) **61273145** e) **61274135**

10) What is the word for **5625415**? ....

a) **STREETS** b) **STARTER** c) **STASHES**
d) **SCATTER** e) **RASHERS**

Chapter Seventeen

LETTER SHIFTS

In these questions, one letter can be moved from the first word to the second word making two new words. The order of the letters must not be changed and the new words must make sense. Write the two new words.

Example:

BRUSH and **IT** become RUSH and BIT

Answer = B

1. Level One

Exercise 17: 1 Write the two new words and the letter that shifts.

Score

1) **TRIED** and **TAP** become .... and ....
   a) **T** b) **R** c) **I** d) **E** e) **D** Answer = ...

2) **WIDTH** and **OWN** become .... and ....
   a) **W** b) **I** c) **D** d) **T** e) **H** Answer = ...

3) **RANGE** and **HER** become .... and ....
   a) **R** b) **A** c) **N** d) **G** e) **E** Answer = ...

4) **DRIVE** and **PAT** become .... and ....
   a) **D** b) **R** c) **I** d) **V** e) **E** Answer = ...

5) **THORN** and **OWN** become .... and ....
   a) **T** b) **H** c) **O** d) **R** e) **N** Answer = ...

6) **EVERY** and **RAG** become .... and ....
   a) **A** b) **Y** c) **E** d) **V** e) **R** Answer = ...

7) **GUEST** and **RID** become .... and ....

a) **G** b) **U** c) **E** d) **S** e) **T** Answer = ...

8) **JOUST** and **SON** become .... and ....

a) **J** b) **O** c) **U** d) **S** e) **T** Answer = ...

9) **BELOW** and **WIN** become .... and ....

a) **B** b) **E** c) **L** d) **O** e) **W** Answer = ...

10) **REBEL** and **OLD** become .... and ....

a) **B** b) **L** c) **O** d) **R** e) **E** Answer = ...

11) **SPURN** and **BAN** become .... and ....

a) **S** b) **P** c) **U** d) **R** e) **N** Answer = ...

12) **BOUND** and **ONCE** become .... and ....

a) **B** b) **O** c) **U** d) **N** e) **D** Answer = ...

13) **DRAWN** and **TOT** become .... and ....

a) **D** b) **R** c) **A** d) **W** e) **N** Answer = ...

14) **FINED** and **ROE** become .... and ....

a) **F** b) **I** c) **N** d) **E** e) **D** Answer = ...

15) **FOUND** and **PUT** become .... and ....

a) **F** b) **O** c) **U** d) **N** e) **D** Answer = ...

16) **CHAMP** and **HOE** become .... and ....

a) **C** b) **H** c) **A** d) **M** e) **P** Answer = ...

17) **CHORE** and **ARC** become .... and ....

a) **C** b) **H** c) **O** d) **R** e) **E** Answer = ...

18) **WEDGE** and **NET** become .... and ....

a) **D** b) **E** c) **G** d) **W** e) **N** Answer = ...

19) **FORAY** and **BUY** become .... and ....

a) **F** b) **O** c) **R** d) **A** e) **Y** Answer = ...

20) **PARTY** and **BUS** become .... and ....

a) **P** b) **A** c) **R** d) **T** e) **Y** Answer = ...

2. Level Two

Exercise 17: 2 Write the two new words and the letter that shifts.

Score

1) **HEART** and **DEER** become .... and ....

a) **H** b) **E** c) **A** d) **R** e) **T** Answer = ...

2) **PAINT** and **RATE** become .... and ....

a) **P** b) **A** c) **I** d) **N** e) **T** Answer = ...

3) **DONOR** and **TINY** become .... and ....

a) **R** b) **I** c) **O** d) **D** e) **N** Answer = ...

4) **TROUT** and **MASH** become .... and ....

a) **U** b) **R** c) **T** d) **M** e) **O** Answer = ...

5) **SHIPS** and **TORN** become .... and ....

a) **P** b) **H** c) **S** d) **O** e) **I** Answer = ...

6) **YEARN** and **NICE** become .... and ....

a) **Y** b) **E** c) **A** d) **R** e) **N** Answer = ...

7) **BREAD** and **ISLE** become .... and ....

a) **B** b) **R** c) **E** d) **A** e) **D** Answer = ...

8) **FLAKE** and **PAST** become .... and ....

a) **F** b) **L** c) **A** d) **K** e) **E** Answer = ...

9) **TWINE** and **BONY** become .... and ....

a) **T** b) **W** c) **I** d) **N** e) **E** Answer = ...

10) **ROUST** and **REIN** become .... and ....

a) **R** b) **O** c) **U** d) **S** e) **T** Answer = ...

11) **GABLE** and **BEAN** become .... and ....

a) **G** b) **A** c) **B** d) **L** e) **E** Answer = ...

12) **ERASE** and **CONE** become .... and ....

a) **E** b) **C** c) **A** d) **S** e) **R** Answer = ...

13) **SHUNT** and **DUTY** become .... and ....

a) **S** b) **H** c) **U** d) **N** e) **T** Answer = ...

14) **BEARD** and **GRIM** become .... and ....

a) **B** b) **E** c) **A** d) **R** e) **D** Answer = ...

15) **RAISE** and **COD** become .... and ....

a) **R** b) **A** c) **I** d) **S** e) **E** Answer = ...

16) **PLAIN** and **QUIT** become .... and ....

a) **P** b) **L** c) **A** d) **I** e) **N** Answer = ...

17) **FAIRY** and **RILE** become .... and ....

a) **F** b) **A** c) **I** d) **R** e) **Y** Answer = ...

18) **HEARD** and **BUY** become .... and ....

a) **H** b) **E** c) **A** d) **R** e) **D** Answer = ...

19) **GRAVE** and **FACE** become .... and ....

a) **G** b) **R** c) **A** d) **V** e) **E** Answer = ...

20) **GRAIN** and **CHAT** become .... and ....

a) **G** b) **R** c) **A** d) **I** e) **N** Answer = ...

3. Level Three

Exercise 17: 3 Write the two new words and the letter that shifts.

1) **CLAMP** and **HEATH** become .... and ....

a) **C** b) **L** c) **A** d) **M** e) **P** Answer = ...

2) **FEAST** and **PITS** become .... and ....

a) **F** b) **E** c) **A** d) **S** e) **T** Answer = ...

3) **WHEAT** and **HUNT** become .... and ....

a) **W** b) **H** c) **E** d) **A** e) **T** Answer = ...

4) **AVOID** and **JUST** become .... and ....

a) **A** b) **V** c) **O** d) **I** e) **D** Answer = ...

5) **LEAST** and **CAME** become .... and ....

a) **L** b) **E** c) **A** d) **S** e) **T** Answer = ...

6) **TOWNS** and **MICE** become .... and ....

a) **T** b) **O** c) **W** d) **N** e) **S** Answer = ...

7) **COAST** and **GAPED** become .... and ....

a) **C** b) **O** c) **A** d) **S** e) **T** Answer = ...

8) **PEARL** and **SHED** become .... and ....

a) **P** b) **E** c) **A** d) **R** e) **L** Answer = ...

9) **TRAMP** and **FOE** become .... and ....

a) **T** b) **R** c) **A** d) **M** e) **P** Answer = ...

10) **CURED** and **WRIT** become .... and ....

a) **C** b) **U** c) **R** d) **E** e) **D** Answer = ...

Chapter Eighteen
COMPOUND WORDS

In these questions find **one** word from **each** group that makes one correctly spelt compound word when joined together. The word from the first group always comes first. Choose **both** words from the options provided and write the new word.

Example:

(no us do) ......no...... and ......on......
(at am on) Answer: ......noon......

1. Level One

Exercise 18: 1 Write the two words and the new compound word.

Score

1) **(had has hot)** .... and ....
(test time take) Answer: ....

a) **had** b) **has** c) **hot** d) **test** e) **time** f) **take**

2) **(end egg eat)** .... and ....
(less laid lisp) Answer: ....

a) **end** b) **egg** c) **eat** d) **less** e) **laid** f) **lisp**

3) **(cab con cot)** .... and ....
(tire tips test) Answer: ....

a) **cab** b) **con** c) **cot** d) **tire** e) **tips** f) **test**

4) **(tick turn type)** .... and ....
(oar own out) Answer: ....

a) **tick** b) **turn** c) **type** d) **oar** e) **own** f) **out**

5) **(any ant arm)** .... and ....
(bind body boat) Answer: ....

a) **any** b) **ant** c) **arm** d) **bind** e) **body** f) **boat**

6) **(dish dash door)** .... and ....
(way wet win) Answer: ....

a) **dish** b) **dash** c) **door** d) **way** e) **wet** f) **win**

7) **(camp less post)** .... and ....
(on it or) Answer: ....

a) **camp** b) **less** c) **post** d) **on** e) **it** f) **or**

8) **(oven open over)** .... and ....
(dip due dot) Answer: ....

a) **oven** b) **open** c) **over** d) **dip** e) **due** f) **dot**

9) **(may mat mix)** .... and ....
(pole pail pond) Answer: ....

a) **may** b) **mat** c) **mix** d) **pole** e) **pail** f) **pond**

10) **(son sin sat)** .... and ....
(kite kind king) Answer: ....

a) **son** b) **sin** c) **sat** d) **kite** e) **kind** f) **king**

11) **(copy cope cool)** .... and ....
(cot cat cup) Answer: ....

a) **copy** b) **cope** c) **cool** d) **cot** e) **cat** f) **cup**

12) **(and art air)** .... and ....
(like lint line) Answer: ....

a) **and** b) **art** c) **air** d) **like** e) **lint** f) **line**

13) **(bed bud bit)** .... and ....
(side sing stun) Answer: ....

a) **bed** b) **bud** c) **bit** d) **side** e) **sing** f) **stun**

14) **(cap con cry)** .... and ....
(tent toss trip) Answer: ....

a) **cap** b) **con** c) **cry** d) **tent** e) **toss** f) **trip**

15) **(wasp went work)** .... and ....
(oar out off) Answer: ....

a) **wasp** b) **went** c) **work** d) **oar** e) **out** f) **off**

16) **(leg lot lad)** .... and ....
(read room raid) Answer: ....

a) **leg** b) **lot** c) **lad** d) **read** e) **room** f) **raid**

17) **(plot play pant)** .... and ....
(pot put pen) Answer: ....

a) **plot** b) **play** c) **pant** d) **pot** e) **put** f) **pen**

18) **(tea top tan)** .... and ....
(sing sign sort) Answer: ....

a) **tea** b) **top** c) **tan** d) **sing** e) **sign** f) **sort**

19) **(cut cat con)** .... and ....
(film fast firm) Answer: ....

a) **cut** b) **cat** c) **con** d) **film** e) **fast** f) **firm**

20) **(mess must mist)** .... and ....
(aim age are) Answer: ....

a) **mess** b) **must** c) **mist** d) **aim** e) **age** f) **are**

2. Level Two

Exercise 18: 2 Write the two words and the new compound word.

Score

1) **(hart pant hand)** .... and ....
(her tin gut) Answer: ....

a) **hart** b) **pant** c) **hand** d) **her** e) **tin** f) **gut**

2) **(now elm ear)** .... and ....
(then rake tile) Answer: ....

a) **now** b) **elm** c) **ear** d) **then** e) **rake** f) **tile**

3) **(cent card clip)** .... and ....
(mean red team) Answer: ....

a) **cent** b) **card** c) **clip** d) **mean** e) **red** f) **team**

4) **(mate good man)** .... and ....
(goes grip girl) Answer: ....

a) **mate** b) **good** c) **man** d) **goes** e) **grip** f) **girl**

5) **(pink plum pelt)** .... and ....
(met king her) Answer: ....

a) **pink** b) **plum** c) **pelt** d) **met** e) **king** f) **her**

6) **(fit fore fly)** .... and ....
(well over ever) Answer: ....

a) **fit** b) **fore** c) **fly** d) **well** e) **over** f) **ever**

7) **(surf sure sort)** .... and ....
(off thing ace) Answer: ....

a) **surf** b) **sure** c) **sort** d) **off** e) **thing** f) **ace**

8) **(grand gran goat)** .... and ....
(day father tea) Answer: ....

a) **grand** b) **gran** c) **goat** d) **day** e) **father** f) **tea**

9) **(out inn oat)** .... and ....
(ring lane rage) Answer: ....

a) **out** b) **inn** c) **oat** d) **ring** e) **lane** f) **rage**

10) **(skip scar soon)** .... and ....
(lit lop let) Answer: ....

a) **skip** b) **scar** c) **soon** d) **lit** e) **lop** f) **let**

11) **(grow bowl gape)** .... and ....
(wing led lit) Answer: ....

a) **grow** b) **bowl** c) **gape** d) **wing** e) **led** f) **lit**

12) **(man dog mar)** .... and ....
(held bled bite) Answer: ....

a) **man** b) **dog** c) **mar** d) **held** e) **bled** f) **bite**

13) **(fine rep pure)** .... and ....
(peat lace line) Answer: ....

a) **fine** b) **rep** c) **pure** d) **peat** e) **lace** f) **line**

14) **(con all now)** .... and ....
(then away done) Answer: ....

a) **con** b) **all** c) **now** d) **then** e) **away** f) **done**

15) **(risk fool pick)** .... and ....
(king led cull) Answer: ....

a) **risk** b) **fool** c) **pick** d) **king** e) **led** f) **cull**

16) **(fine fin fun)** .... and ....
(ally time alley) Answer: ....

a) **fine** b) **fin** c) **fun** d) **ally** e) **time** f) **alley**

17) **(pocket little snip)** .... and ....
(pet one snap) Answer: ....

a) **pocket** b) **little** c) **snip** d) **pet** e) **one** f) **snap**

18) **(tee don tone)** .... and ....
(ate ore sing) Answer: ....

a) **tee** b) **don** c) **tone** d) **ate** e) **ore** f) **sing**

19) **(lot many fuss)** .... and ....
(uses use her) Answer: ....

a) **lot** b) **many** c) **fuss** d) **uses** e) **use** f) **her**

20) **(verb kerb back)** .... and ....
(bail one ally) Answer: ....

a) **verb** b) **kerb** c) **back** d) **bail** e) **one** f) **ally**

3. Level Three

Exercise 18: 3 Write the two words and the new compound word.

Score

1) **(fore old for)** .... and ....
(ages den you) Answer: ....

a) **fore** b) **old** c) **for** d) **ages** e) **den** f) **you**

2) **(ruby hove blood)** .... and ....
(died wax red) Answer: ....

a) **ruby** b) **hove** c) **blood** d) **died** e) **wax** f) **red**

3) **(code paste mode)** .... and ....
(ding sty try) Answer: ....

a) **code** b) **paste** c) **mode** d) **ding** e) **sty** f) **try**

4) **(ear this hard)** .... and ....
(shot done dear) Answer: ....

a) **ear** b) **this** c) **hard** d) **shot** e) **done** f) **dear**

5) **(bee boa always)** .... and ....
(late sting there) Answer: ....
a) **bee** b) **boa** c) **always** d) **late** e) **sting** f) **there**

6) **(mod cheap mode)** .... and ....
(rate pest den) Answer: ....
a) **mod** b) **cheap** c) **mode** d) **rate** e) **pest** f) **den**

7) **(car cove rag)** .... and ....
(tern rage bull) Answer: ....
a) **car** b) **cove** c) **rag** d) **tern** e) **rage** f) **bull**

8) **(end and sun)** .... and ....
(lest danger anger) Answer: ....
a) **end** b) **and** c) **sun** d) **lest** e) **danger** f) **anger**

9) **(note not white)** .... and ....
(icy icing taking) Answer: ....
a) **note** b) **not** c) **white** d) **icy** e) **icing** f) **taking**

10) **(lye ire react)** .... and ....
(on ion cheese) Answer: ....
a) **lye** b) **ire** c) **react** d) **on** e) **ion** f) **cheese**

Chapter Nineteen
HIDDEN WORDS

In these sentences, a hidden four-letter word can be found at the **end** of one word and the **beginning** of the next word. Choose the two words from the sentence provided and write the hidden word.

Example:

They couldn't see the **bat h**iding.

Two Words: bat hiding Answer: bath

1. Level One

Exercise 19: 1 Find the hidden word and write the two words it was made from.

Score

1) I like the big old house.

Two Words: .... Answer: ....

a) **I like** b) **like the** c) **the big** d) **big old** e) **old house**

2) Log in first, then press enter.

Two Words: .... Answer: ....

a) **Log in** b) **in first** c) **first then** d) **then press** e) **press enter**

3) Your plan is a great idea.

Two Words: .... Answer: ....

a) **Your plan** b) **plan is** c) **is a** d) **a great** e) **great idea**

4) Place the whisk in the bowl.

Two Words: .... Answer: ....

a) **Place the** b) **the whisk** c) **whisk in** d) **in the** e) **the bowl**

5) The little mouse ate the cheese.

Two Words: .... Answer: ....

a) **The little** b) **little mouse** c) **mouse ate**
d) **ate the** e) **the cheese**

6) We helped father repair the motorbike.

Two Words: .... Answer: ....

a) **We helped** b) **helped father** c) **father repair**
d) **repair the** e) **the motorbike**

7) Mother decided to take a break.

Two Words: .... Answer: ....

a) **Mother decided** b) **decided to** c) **to take**
d) **take a** e) **a break**

8) The time is ten to eleven.

Two Words: .... Answer: ....

a) **The time** b) **time is** c) **is ten**
d) **ten to** e) **to eleven**

9) There's no telling where he's been.

Two Words: .... Answer: ....

a) **There's no** b) **no telling** c) **telling where**
d) **where he's** e) **he's been**

10) Thin ice can be extremely dangerous.

Two Words: .... Answer: ....

a) **Thin ice** b) **ice can** c) **can be**
d) **be extremely** e) **extremely dangerous**

11) Now wash and dry your hands.

Two Words: .... Answer: ....

a) **Now wash** b) **wash and** c) **and dry**
d) **dry your** e) **your hands**

12) There is a good disco later.

Two Words: .... Answer: ....

a) **There is** b) **is a** c) **a good**
d) **good disco** e) **disco later**

13) The red apple was very tasty.

Two Words: .... Answer: ....

a) **The red** b) **red apple** c) **apple was**
d) **was very** e) **very tasty**

14) I went fishing for my supper.

Two Words: .... Answer: ....

a) **I went** b) **went fishing** c) **fishing for**
d) **for my** e) **my supper**

15) The team asked for our help.

Two Words: .... Answer: ....

a) **The team** b) **team asked** c) **asked for**
d) **for our** e) **our help**

16) This old coat is very dirty.

Two Words: .... Answer: ....

a) **This old** b) **old coat** c) **coat is**
d) **is very** e) **very dirty**

17) My son goes to piano lessons.

Two Words: .... Answer: ....

a) **My son** b) **son goes** c) **goes to**
d) **to piano** e) **piano lessons**

18) There's a dead wasp in there.

Two Words: .... Answer: ....

a) **There's a** b) **a dead** c) **dead wasp**
d) **wasp in** e) **in there**

19) That ape is looking at us.

Two Words: .... Answer: ....

a) **That ape** b) **ape is** c) **is looking**
d) **looking at** e) **at us**

20) Her test marks are so low.

Two Words: .... Answer: ....

a) **Her test** b) **test marks** c) **marks are**
d) **are so** e) **so low**

2. Level Two

Exercise 19: 2 Write the hidden word and the two words it was made from.

Score

1) "Walk this way," called the teacher.

Two Words: .... Answer: ....

a) **Walk this** b) **this way** c) **way called**
d) **called the** e) **the teacher**

2) The cute little puppy was poorly.

Two Words: .... Answer: ....

a) **The cute** b) **cute little** c) **little puppy**
d) **puppy was** e) **was poorly**

3) Will you close that window please?

Two Words: .... Answer: ....

a) **Will you** b) **you close** c) **close that**
d) **that window** e) **window please**

4) This carpet will need cleaning soon.

Two Words: .... Answer: ....

a) **This carpet** b) **carpet will** c) **will need**
d) **need cleaning** e) **cleaning soon**

5) Please take those empty bottles away.

Two Words: .... Answer: ....

a) **Please take** b) **take those** c) **those empty**
d) **empty bottles** e) **bottles away**

6) "Hold that rod tight!" he shouted.

Two Words: .... Answer: ....

a) **Hold that** b) **that rod** c) **rod tight**
d) **tight he** e) **he shouted**

7) Choose which effect you like best.

Two Words: .... Answer: ....

a) **Choose which** b) **which effect** c) **effect you**
d) **you like** e) **like best**

8) That long ride was really good!

Two Words: .... Answer: ....

a) **That long** b) **long ride** c) **ride was**
d) **was really** e) **really good**

9) Place the dish inside the oven.

Two Words: .... Answer: ....

a) **Place the** b) **the dish** c) **dish inside**
d) **inside the** e) **the oven**

10) They carefully crossed over the water.

Two Words: .... Answer: ....

a) **They carefully** b) **carefully crossed** c) **crossed over**
d) **over the** e) **the water**

11) They're always planning their next holiday.

Two Words: .... Answer: ....

a) **They're always** b) **always planning**
c) **planning their** d) **their next** e) **next holiday**

12) What time should the taxi arrive?

Two Words: .... Answer: ....

a) **What time** b) **time should** c) **should the**
d) **the taxi** e) **taxi arrive**

13) Come away from the window, now!

Two Words: .... Answer: ....

a) **Come away** b) **away from** c) **from the**
d) **the window** e) **window now**

14) Will they win every single trophy?

Two Words: .... Answer: ....

a) **Will they** b) **they win** c) **win every**
d) **every single** e) **single trophy**

15) This ink has stained the cloth.

Two Words: .... Answer: ....

a) **This ink** b) **ink has** c) **has stained**
d) **stained the** e) **the cloth**

16) They are attempting the world record.

Two Words: .... Answer: ....

a) **They are** b) **are attempting** c) **attempting the**
d) **the world** e) **world record**

17) The kettle appeared to be boiling.

Two Words: .... Answer: ....

a) **The kettle** b) **kettle appeared** c) **appeared to**
d) **to be** e) **be boiling**

18) Have you recently applied for work?

Two Words: .... Answer: ....

a) **Have you** b) **you recently** c) **recently applied**
d) **applied for** e) **for work**

19) Double the quantity for twelve people.

Two Words: .... Answer: ....

a) **Double the** b) **the quantity** c) **quantity for**
d) **for twelve** e) **twelve people**

20) They earned sixteen pounds pocket money.

Two Words: .... Answer: ....

a) **They earned** b) **earned sixteen** c) **sixteen pounds**
d) **pounds pocket** e) **pocket money**

3. Level Three

Score

Exercise 19: 3 Write the hidden word and the two words it was made from.

1) Make pickles with seasonal garden produce.

Two Words: .... Answer: ....

a) **Make pickles** b) **pickles with** c) **with seasonal**
d) **seasonal garden** e) **garden produce**

2) They have almost everything they need.

Two Words: .... Answer: ....

a) **They have** b) **have almost** c) **almost everything**
d) **everything they** e) **they need**

3) Mike and Angela quarrelled about everything.

Two Words: .... Answer: ....

a) **Mike and** b) **and Angela** c) **Angela quarrelled**
d) **quarrelled about** e) **about everything**

4) The plumber will unclog our drains.

Two Words: .... Answer: ....

a) **The plumber** b) **plumber will** c) **will unclog**
d) **unclog our** e) **our drains**

5) For chesty relief try natural remedies.

Two Words: .... Answer: ....

a) **For chesty** b) **chesty relief** c) **relief try**
d) **try natural** e) **natural remedies**

6) Herbal medicine contains only organic ingredients.

Two Words: .... Answer: ....

a) **Herbal medicine** b) **medicine contains**
c) **contains only** d) **only organic** e) **organic ingredients**

7) Alone; only solitude, isolation and loneliness.

Two Words: .... Answer: ....

a) **Alone only** b) **only solitude** c) **solitude isolation**
d) **isolation and** e) **and loneliness**

8) Swarms of locusts have invaded farmland.

Two Words: .... Answer: ....

a) **Swarms of** b) **of locusts** c) **locusts have**
d) **have invaded** e) **invaded farmland**

9) "People donated generously," said the chairman.

Two Words: .... Answer: ....

a) **People donated** b) **donated generously**
c) **generously said** d) **said the** e) **the chairman**

10) This wooden chair isn't very comfortable.

Two Words: .... Answer: ....

a) **This wooden** b) **wooden chair** c) **chair isn't**
d) **isn't very** e) **very comfortable**

Chapter Twenty
MISSING LETTERS

In these questions the **same** letter will fit into **both** sets of brackets, to end the word in front of the brackets and start the word after the brackets. Write the correct letter that completes all four words.

Example:

tea [?] akes

fro [?] op Answer: ....m....

(The four words are **team**, **makes**, **from** and **mop**.)

1. Level One

Exercise 20: 1 Write the letter that will end the first word and start the second.

Score

1) **blo [?] ire**
cre [?] ent
Answer: ....
a) **r** b) **b** c) **w** d) **f** e) **h**

2) **fac [?] ack**
cos [?] ear
Answer: ....
a) **e** b) **b** c) **h** d) **t** e) **y**

3) **war [?] ext**
spi [?] oun
Answer: ....
a) **c** b) **e** c) **s** d) **r** e) **n**

4) **her [?] ugs**
sta [?] ead
Answer: ....
a) **s** b) **r** c) **b** d) **t** e) **h**

5) **ban [?] ale**
sin [?] low

Answer: ....

a) **k** b) **g** c) **f** d) **t** e) **p**

6) **bus [?] awn**
fur [?] ear

Answer: ....

a) **h** b) **l** c) **t** d) **y** e) **p**

7) **eve [?] ain**
dee [?] ide

Answer: ....

a) **n** b) **p** c) **t** d) **r** e) **d**

8) **pin [?] ime**
pos [?] eam

Answer: ....

a) **k** b) **e** c) **t** d) **l** e) **s**

9) **wee [?] ick**
pac [?] ing

Answer: ....

a) **e** b) **s** c) **t** d) **l** e) **k**

10) **tun [?] ged**
sag [?] unt

Answer: ....

a) **g** b) **a** c) **h** d) **e** e) **s**

11) **ben [?] ear**
car [?] amp

Answer: ....

a) **h** b) **l** c) **r** d) **d** e) **f**

12) **fla [?] rey**
gri [?] ush

Answer: ....

a) **y** b) **d** c) **r** d) **t** e) **p**

13) **min [?] ind** Answer: ....

pin [?] ept a) **e** b) **d** c) **k** d) **m** e) **w**

14) **lea [?] eat** Answer: ....

cor [?] ine a) **r** b) **f** c) **e** d) **n** e) **s**

15) **ove [?] est** Answer: ....

mea [?] ose a) **r** b) **t** c) **w** d) **p** e) **n**

16) **rea [?] isk** Answer: ....

roa [?] ush a) **p** b) **r** c) **d** d) **w** e) **m**

17) **tap [?] alt** Answer: ....

las [?] ure a) **e** b) **t** c) **s** d) **h** e) **b**

18) **dar [?] ast** Answer: ....

har [?] ars a) **t** b) **k** c) **p** d) **e** e) **d**

19) **loa [?] ire** Answer: ....

lea [?] old a) **t** b) **d** c) **w** d) **f** e) **c**

20) **hea [?] ear** Answer: ....

spi [?] one a) **d** b) **l** c) **t** d) **n** e) **p**

2. Level Two

Exercise 20: 2 Write the letter that will end the first word and start the second.

Score

1) **grow** [?] **ames** Answer: ....
gree [?] **ight**
a) **d** b) **l** c) **g** d) **t** e) **n**

2) **lan** [?] **ites** Answer: ....
whis [?] **ilts**
a) **g** b) **d** c) **k** d) **w** e) **e**

3) **ease** [?] **east** Answer: ....
came [?] **abel**
a) **b** b) **d** c) **y** d) **l** e) **c**

4) **buil** [?] **arts** Answer: ....
chea [?] **each**
a) **d** b) **p** c) **r** d) **k** e) **t**

5) **thin** [?] **race** Answer: ....
stun [?] **owns**
a) **t** b) **g** c) **k** d) **e** e) **s**

6) **ree** [?] **ear** Answer: ....
pro [?] **rab**
a) **p** b) **g** c) **d** d) **l** e) **m**

7) **brin** [?] **ight** Answer: ....
awar [?] **vent**
a) **g** b) **d** c) **n** d) **e** e) **t**

8) **frie** [?] **ings** Answer: ....
joke [?] **oast**
a) **s** b) **d** c) **w** d) **c** e) **r**

9) **shar [?] ager**
tens [?] very

Answer: ....

a) **l** b) **e** c) **k** d) **t** e) **d**

10) **brie [?] able**
shel [?] ence

Answer: ....

a) **t** b) **c** c) **p** d) **f** e) **l**

11) **swee [?] each**
chea [?] edal

Answer: ....

a) **t** b) **m** c) **r** d) **b** e) **p**

12) **basi [?] late**
crie [?] hare

Answer: ....

a) **p** b) **c** c) **d** d) **s** e) **t**

13) **ange [?] east**
civi [?] ight

Answer: ....

a) **r** b) **c** c) **l** d) **b** e) **s**

14) **ver [?] ury**
com [?] one

Answer: ....

a) **y** b) **f** c) **t** d) **b** e) **e**

15) **clu [?] ven**
bar [?] ast

Answer: ....

a) **b** b) **v** c) **n** d) **l** e) **e**

16) **bal [?] ark**
cla [?] ate

Answer: ....

a) **p** b) **d** c) **e** d) **r** e) **l**

17) **clea** [?] **oise** Answer: ....
chai [?] **urse**
a) **r** b) **p** c) **n** d) **s** e) **t**

18) **peac** [?] **appy** Answer: ....
clas [?] **ound**
a) **e** b) **p** c) **n** d) **r** e) **h**

19) **shee** [?] **aces** Answer: ....
tape [?] **adar**
a) **p** b) **l** c) **d** d) **r** e) **s**

20) **come** [?] **runk** Answer: ....
deal [?] **aunt**
a) **d** b) **s** c) **t** d) **h** e) **i**

3. Level Three

Exercise 20: 3 Write the letter that will end the first word and start the second.

1) **calle** [?] **rains** Answer: ....
dashe [?] **ecked**
a) **r** b) **s** c) **d** d) **p** e) **g**

2) **pris** [?] **anor** Answer: ....
scra [?] **ight**
a) **e** b) **t** c) **p** d) **m** e) **n**

3) **chim** [?] **salm** Answer: ....
gras [?] **itch**
a) **e** b) **s** c) **w** d) **h** e) **p**

4) **tub** [?] **rea**
fle [?] **cre**

Answer: ....

a) **e** b) **w** c) **a** d) **s** e) **t**

5) **squa** [?] **afer**
thre [?] **ands**

Answer: ....

a) **s** b) **h** c) **w** d) **t** e) **l**

6) **chase** [?] **ocket**
ruler [?] **immer**

Answer: ....

a) **d** b) **r** c) **l** d) **p** e) **s**

7) **tease** [?] **eaper**
packe [?] **acket**

Answer: ....

a) **d** b) **s** c) **p** d) **r** e) **j**

8) **softe** [?] **ation**
worse [?] **estle**

Answer: ....

a) **r** b) **t** c) **n** d) **y** e) **s**

9) **bloo** [?] **anger**
foru [?] **onkey**

Answer: ....

a) **d** b) **e** c) **m** d) **r** e) **s**

10) **kindl** [?] **early**
baker [?] **elped**

Answer: ....

a) **e** b) **n** c) **h** d) **y** e) **s**

Chapter Twenty-one
ANALOGIES

In these questions, find **one** word from **each** group that will complete the analogy in the best way. Choose **both** words from the options provided.

Example:

kid is to (child goat glove) ....goat..........
as **foal** is to (drink horse blanket) ....horse..........

1. Level One

Exercise 21: 1 Write the two words that complete the analogy.

Score

1) **Petal** is to (grass flower pot) ....
as **leaf** is to (cup tree earth) ....

a) **grass** b) **flower** c) **pot** d) **cup** e) **tree** f) **earth**

2) **Duck** is to (pen water feathers) ....
as **cat** is to (fur wave stroke) ....

a) **pen** b) **water** c) **feathers** d) **fur** e) **wave** f) **stroke**

3) **Uncle** is to (cousin boy adult) ....
as **aunty** is to (girl friend relative) ....

a) **cousin** b) **boy** c) **adult** d) **girl** e) **friend** f) **relative**

4) **Piglet** is to (honk cub pig) ....
as **kitten** is to (paw cat baby) ....

a) **honk** b) **cub** c) **pig** d) **paw** e) **cat** f) **baby**

5) **Skip** is to (run rope play) ....
as **bounce** is to (round toys ball) ....

a) **run** b) **rope** c) **play** d) **round** e) **toys** f) **ball**

6) **Lace** is to (shoe sandal foot) ....
as **button** is to (needle shirt scarf) ....

a) **shoe** b) **sandal** c) **foot** d) **needle** e) **shirt** f) **scarf**

7) **Ear** is to (mouth listen startle) ....
as **nose** is to (smell food eat) ....

a) **mouth** b) **listen** c) **startle** d) **smell** e) **food** f) **eat**

8) **Snap** is to (branch climb break) ....
as **mend** is to (smash fix hurt) ....

a) **branch** b) **climb** c) **break** d) **smash** e) **fix** f) **hurt**

9) **Short** is to (tall span take) ....
as **blind** is to (eye seen sighted) ....

a) **tall** b) **span** c) **take** d) **eye** e) **seen** f) **sighted**

10) **Six** is to (seven even multiply) ....
as **three** is to (dice thrice odd) ....

a) **seven** b) **even** c) **multiply** d) **dice** e) **thrice** f) **odd**

11) **Snow** is to (ski ice skate) ....
as **water** is to (splash surf wave) ....

a) **ski** b) **ice** c) **skate** d) **splash** e) **surf** f) **wave**

12) **Rose** is to (red garden flower) ....

as **mint** is to (herb taste eat) ....

a) **red** b) **garden** c) **flower** d) **herb** e) **taste** f) **eat**

13) **Tar** is to (rat road black) ....

as **but** is to (tub join think) ....

a) **rat** b) **road** c) **black** d) **tub** e) **join** f) **think**

14) **Lion** is to (lettuce meat hunt) ....

as **cow** is to (milk leaves grass) ....

a) **lettuce** b) **meat** c) **hunt** d) **milk** e) **leaves** f) **grass**

15) **Four** is to (foe eight fore) ....

as **maid** is to (made servant mode) ....

a) **foe** b) **eight** c) **fore** d) **made** e) **servant** f) **mode**

16) **Sun** is to (planet day dark) ....

as **moon** is to (crescent night sky) ....

a) **planet** b) **day** c) **dark** d) **crescent** e) **night** f) **sky**

17) **Loud** is to (shout voice mouth) ....

as **quiet** is to (quite peace whisper) ....

a) **shout** b) **voice** c) **mouth** d) **quite** e) **peace** f) **whisper**

18) **Pen** is to (scratch ink wood) ....

as **pencil** is to (lead picture school) ....

a) **scratch** b) **ink** c) **wood** d) **lead** e) **picture** f) **school**

19) **Car** is to (ignition steer road) ....
as **train** is to (carriage track guard) ....

a) **ignition** b) **steer** c) **road** d) **carriage** e) **track** f) **guard**

20) **Tiny** is to (small baby dust) ....
as **huge** is to (bridge large medium) ....

a) **small** b) **baby** c) **dust** d) **bridge** e) **large** f) **medium**

2. Level Two

Exercise 21: 2 Write the two words that complete the analogy.

Score

1) **Check** is to (money cheque coin) ....
as **quay** is to (piano play key) ....

a) **money** b) **cheque** c) **coin** d) **piano** e) **play** f) **key**

2) **Cod** is to (haddock fish sea) ....
as **collie** is to (dog meat sheep) ....

a) **haddock** b) **fish** c) **sea** d) **dog** e) **meat** f) **sheep**

3) **Gosling** is to (goose duck fly) ....
as **cub** is to (rabbit beaver bear) ....

a) **goose** b) **duck** c) **fly** d) **rabbit** e) **beaver** f) **bear**

4) **Reed** is to (book read magazine) ....
as **rain** is to (reign shower wet) ....

a) **book** b) **read** c) **magazine** d) **reign** e) **shower** f) **wet**

5) **Knife** is to (cutletry fork sharp) ....
as **plate** is to (eat dinner crockery) ....

a) **cutlery** b) **fork** c) **sharp** d) **eat** e) **dinner** f) **crockery**

6) **Moth** is to (butterfly caterpillar wings) ....
as **toad** is to (tadpole pupa lizard) ....

a) **butterfly** b) **caterpillar** c) **wings** d) **tadpole** e) **pupa** f) **lizard**

7) **Ring** is to (telephone circle finger) ....
as **watch** is to (time wrist hands) ....

a) **telephone** b) **circle** c) **finger** d) **time** e) **wrist** f) **hands**

8) **Forward** is to (advance march move) ....
as **backward** is to (slow step retreat) ....

a) **advance** b) **march** c) **move** d) **slow** e) **step** f) **retreat**

9) **Swede** is to (weed country vegetable) ....
as **mango** is to (fruit tango chutney) ....

a) **weed** b) **country** c) **vegetable** d) **fruit** e) **tango** f) **chutney**

10) **Denim** is to (mined jeans jacket) ....
as **strap** is to (trap safety parts) ....

a) **mined** b) **jeans** c) **jacket** d) **trap** e) **safety** f) **parts**

11) **Ankle** is to (leg bone joint) ....
as **arm** is to (muscle limb elbow) ....

a) **leg** b) **bone** c) **joint** d) **muscle** e) **limb** f) **elbow**

12) **Black** is to (brown bird ink) ....

as **gold** is to (fish colour rich) ....

a) **brown** b) **bird** c) **ink** d) **fish** e) **colour** f) **rich**

13) **Football** is to (goal ball pitch) ....

as **basketball** is to (score team court) ....

a) **goal** b) **ball** c) **pitch** d) **score** e) **team** f) **court**

14) **Ancient** is to (old elderly world) ....

as **modern** is to (city new antique) ....

a) **old** b) **elderly** c) **world** d) **city** e) **new** f) **antique**

15) **Timber** is to (copse wood cloth) ....

as **fabric** is to (material dress conditioner) ....

a) **copse** b) **wood** c) **cloth** d) **material** e) **dress** f) **conditioner**

16) **Canine** is to (tooth horse dog) ....

as **feline** is to (female cat wolf) ....

a) **tooth** b) **horse** c) **dog** d) **female** e) **cat** f) **wolf**

17) **Ate** is to (eight eat food) ....

as **boy** is to (man girl buoy) ....

a) **eight** b) **eat** c) **food** d) **man** e) **girl** f) **buoy**

18) **Car** is to (drive steer boot) ....

as **bicycle** is to (race wheel ride) ....

a) **drive** b) **steer** c) **boot** d) **race** e) **wheel** f) **ride**

19) **Drink** is to (water straw cup) ....
as **eat** is to (hungry fork ate) ....

a) **water** b) **straw** c) **cup** d) **hungry** e) **fork** f) **ate**

20) **Groom** is to (brush man broom) ....
as **bride** is to (lady wedding dress) ....

a) **brush** b) **man** c) **broom** d) **lady** e) **wedding** f) **dress**

3. Level Three

Score

Exercise 21: 3 Write the two words that complete the analogy.

1) **Mobile** is to (moving phone stop) ....
as **stationary** is to (static stationery electric) ....

a) **moving** b) **phone** c) **stop** d) **static** e) **stationery** f) **electric**

2) **Thyme** is to (time herb clock) ....
as **cumin** is to (enter fruit spice) ....

a) **time** b) **herb** c) **clock** d) **enter** e) **fruit** f) **spice**

3) **Chicken** is to (poultry cockerel coop) ....
as **bee** is to (honey hive sting) ....

a) **poultry** b) **cockerel** c) **coop** d) **honey** e) **hive** f) **sting**

4) **Desert** is to (dessert abandon sand) ....
as **remain** is to (keep stay leave) ....

a) **dessert** b) **abandon** c) **sand** d) **keep** e) **stay** f) **leave**

5) **Manner** is to (polite manor behaviour) ....
as **cygnet** is to (swan tobacco signet) ....
a) **polite** b) **manor** c) **behaviour** d) **swan** e) **tobacco** f) **signet**

6) **Tea** is to (break drink leaf) ....
as **coffee** is to (brown bean powder) ....
a) **break** b) **drink** c) **leaf** d) **brown** e) **bean** f) **powder**

7) **Head** is to (goggles balaclava skull) ....
as **hand** is to (knuckle mitten ring) ....
a) **goggles** b) **balaclava** c) **skull** d) **knuckle** e) **mitten** f) **ring**

8) **Goose** is to (flock gaggle duck) ....
as **elephant** is to (herd tusk trunk) ....
a) **flock** b) **gaggle** c) **duck** d) **herd** e) **tusk** f) **trunk**

9) **Eccles** is to (slice sweet cake) ....
as **digestive** is to (stomach biscuit meal) ....
a) **slice** b) **sweet** c) **cake** d) **stomach** e) **biscuit** f) **meal**

10) **Reward** is to (money wanted drawer) ....
as **tenner** is to (rennet pound notes) ....
a) **money** b) **wanted** c) **drawer** d) **rennet** e) **pound** f) **notes**

Notes

Answers

Chapter Eleven
Letter Sequencing

Exercise 11: 1

1) RO
2) NR
3) KM
4) JI
5) LK
6) RY
7) PI
8) NA
9) QT
10) EA
11) IH
12) FD
13) JK
14) MU
15) LJ
16) TQ
17) LF
18) JK
19) SR
20) TH

Exercise 11: 2

1) RI
2) JC
3) DS
4) IG
5) DS
6) PW
7) GU
8) IP
9) UK
10) MS
11) NR
12) UX
13) UE
14) VA
15) VU
16) XO
17) OE
18) TZ
19) JX
20) YF

Exercise 11: 3

1) HI
2) VK
3) OM
4) VW
5) TP
6) SG
7) MH
8) PF
9) LJ
10) UN

Chapter Twelve
Alphabet Codes

Exercise 12: 1

1) UL
2) XB
3) QA
4) PN
5) YJ
6) LI
7) PH
8) FP
9) NB
10) LT
11) HV
12) YF
13) SD
14) QK
15) IZ
16) RV
17) AN
18) JR
19) OM
20) DV

Exercise 12: 2

1) DH
2) CI
3) MY
4) BB
5) BW
6) LA
7) CW
8) AA
9) UA
10) SX
11) EX
12) BA
13) EM
14) ZA
15) CG
16) QY
17) VL
18) CF
19) XU
20) CX

Exercise 12: 3

1) AD
2) EY
3) XX
4) AC
5) YV
6) CV
7) QF
8) RD
9) GP
10) JV

Chapter Thirteen
More Alphabet Codes

Exercise 13: 1

1) IFMQ
2) JMQR
3) HGJH
4) KBTP
5) NMQR
6) QHCD
7) PLON
8) JCKT
9) DRIM
10) GJMN
11) APCU
12) DQWV
13) LQKP
14) VHMC
15) HFKD
16) IPMF
17) RSPL
18) UDLO
19) VHMD
20) TCUJ

Exercise 13: 2

1) GUDIW
2) GLAZE
3) GTLZM
4) IMAGE
5) KCJML
6) NURSE
7) WHDUV
8) RADIO
9) YHLOV
10) EXTRA
11) ZEYAZ
12) JQPGA
13) WORSE
14) DAUNT
15) RMGBV
16) ANCJS
17) BISHOP
18) FLOAT
19) SCORED
20) TRUSTY

Exercise 13: 3

1) DHBYO
2) CTFCDJ
3) FRUIT
4) ZDHFDU
5) WRERMV
6) BLRZM
7) QAYPCZ

Answers

8) REWARD
9) AWFUL
10) XRIXFH

Chapter Fourteen
One Word Patterns

Exercise 14: 1

1) sun
2) law
3) ash
4) car
5) din
6) ate
7) tag
8) tan
9) tow
10) art
11) shin
12) trap
13) prod
14) came
15) tide
16) rate
17) pied
18) silt
19) hare
20) tear

Exercise 14: 2

1) farm
2) shut
3) sure
4) seal
5) tone
6) thug
7) ever
8) hunt
9) ewer
10) rail
11) heat
12) dent
13) mare
14) sear
15) menu
16) bard
17) tiny
18) emit
19) acre
20) toad

Exercise 14: 3

1) seam
2) moon
3) scar
4) heel
5) pine
6) seed
7) lead
8) dear
9) nice
10) roar

Chapter Fifteen
Two Word Patterns

Exercise 15: 1

1) posh
2) byre
3) path
4) lamb
5) lisp
6) held
7) sail
8) memo
9) rein
10) gilt
11) tuna
12) hero
13) veto
14) lawn
15) lent
16) yard
17) lime
18) tour
19) spar
20) push

Exercise 15: 2

1) star
2) tsar
3) soil
4) epee
5) pest
6) word
7) scan
8) tent
9) sell
10) pray
11) sire
12) moat
13) urge
14) tide
15) limb
16) acre
17) pity
18) idle
19) soft
20) tart

Exercise 15: 3

1) piano
2) poor
3) tense
4) coax
5) ache
6) oven
7) point
8) worn
9) soul
10) brae

Chapter Sixteen
Secret Codes

Exercise 16: 1

1) 2154
2) 2335
3) 2412352
4) 5126
5) 24636
6) 51365
7) 2562
8) 624315
9) 634251
10) 6257
11) 461257
12) 3561472
13) 6732
14) 21357
15) 3541276
16) 7453
17) 62534
18) 7256143
19) 2413
20) 41352

Exercise 16: 2

1) 3573
2) SHARE
3) 4376251
4) 4126
5) BLADE
6) 1325416
7) 3541
8) POLEMIC
9) 3173418
10) 6521
11) TEASE
12) 3265314
13) 5167
14) WHEEL
15) 3716524
16) 4215
17) STEAMY
18) 4276153
19) 7113
20) 3567413

Exercise 16: 3

1) 6246
2) RELEASE
3) 5213674
4) 5432
5) READER

Answers

6) 31245216
7) 5123
8) HEATER
9) 61274135
10) STASHES

Chapter Seventeen
Letter Shifts

Exercise 17: 1

1) TIDE & TRAP (R)
2) WITH & DOWN (D)
3) RANG & HERE (E)
4) DIVE & PART (R)
5) HORN & TOWN (T)
6) VERY & RAGE (E)
7) GUST & RIDE (E)
8) JUST & SOON (O)
9) BLOW & WINE (E)
10) REEL & BOLD (B)
11) SPUN & BARN (R)
12) BOND & OUNCE (U)
13) DAWN & TROT (R)
14) FINE & RODE (D)
15) FUND & POUT (O)
16) CHAP & HOME (M)
17) CORE & ARCH (H)
18) EDGE & NEWT (W)
19) FRAY & BUOY (O)
20) PART & BUSY (Y)

Exercise 17: 2

1) HEAR & DETER (T)
2) PANT & IRATE (I)
3) DOOR & TINNY (N)
4) TOUT & MARSH (R)
5) SIPS & THORN (H)
6) YARN & NIECE (E)
7) BRED & AISLE (A)
8) FLAK & PASTE (E)
9) TWIN & EBONY (E)
10) ROUT & REINS (S)
11) ABLE & BEGAN (G)
12) EASE & CRONE (R)
13) HUNT & DUSTY (S)
14) BARD & GRIME (E)
15) RISE & CODA (A)
16) PAIN & QUILT (L)
17) AIRY & RIFLE (F)
18) HEAD & BURY (R)
19) GAVE & FARCE (R)
20) GAIN & CHART (R)

Exercise 17: 3

1) CAMP & HEALTH (L)
2) FEAT & SPITS (S)
3) WHET & HAUNT (A)
4) AVID & JOUST (O)
5) EAST & CAMEL (L)
6) TOWS & MINCE (N)
7) COAT & GASPED (S)
8) PEAL & SHRED (R)
9) TAMP & FORE (R)
10) CURD & WRITE (E)

Chapter Eighteen
Compound Words

Exercise 18: 1

1) hottest
2) endless
3) contest
4) turnout
5) anybody
6) doorway
7) lesson
8) overdue
9) maypole
10) sinking
11) copycat
12) airline
13) bedside
14) content
15) workout
16) legroom
17) playpen
18) teasing
19) confirm
20) message

Exercise 18: 2

1) panther
2) earthen
3) centred
4) mangoes
5) plummet
6) flyover
7) surface
8) grandfather
9) outrage
10) scarlet
11) growled
12) marbled
13) replace
14) condone
15) pickled
16) finally
17) snippet
18) donate
19) lotuses
20) verbally

Exercise 18: 3

1) forages
2) hovered
3) modesty
4) earshot
5) boasting
6) moderate
7) coverage
8) endanger
9) noticing
10) reaction

Chapter Nineteen
Hidden Words

Exercise 19: 1

1) gold
2) sent
3) tide
4) skin
5) seat

Answers

6) them
7) herd
8) tent
9) note
10) nice
11) hand
12) cola
13) here
14) form
15) mask
16) sold
17) song
18) spin
19) tape
20) solo

Exercise 19: 2

1) sway
2) wasp
3) twin
4) scar
5) seem
6) trod
7) chef
8) grid
9) shin
10) dove
11) real
12) mesh
13) down
14) wine
15) sink
16) area
17) leap
18) your
19) fort
20) year

Exercise 19: 3

1) epic
2) veal
3) aqua
4) logo
5) tyre
6) balm
7) neon
8) vein
9) edge
10) iris

Chapter Twenty
Missing Letters

Exercise 20: 1

1) w
2) t
3) n
4) b
5) g
6) y
7) r
8) t
9) k
10) a
11) d
12) p
13) k
14) n
15) n
16) r
17) s
18) e
19) f
20) t

Exercise 20: 2

1) n
2) k
3) l
4) t
5) g
6) d
7) e
8) r
9) e
10) f
11) p
12) s
13) l
14) b
15) e
16) d
17) n
18) h
19) r
20) t

Exercise 20: 3

1) d
2) m
3) p
4) a
5) w
6) s
7) r
8) n
9) m
10) y

Chapter Twenty-one
Analogies

Exercise 21: 1

1) flower tree
2) feathers fur
3) boy girl
4) pig cat
5) rope ball
6) shoe shirt
7) listen smell
8) break fix
9) tall sighted
10) even odd
11) ski surf
12) flower herb
13) rat tub
14) meat grass
15) fore made
16) day night
17) shout whisper
18) ink lead
19) road track
20) small large

Exercise 21: 2

1) cheque key
2) fish dog
3) goose bear
4) read reign
5) cutlery crockery
6) caterpillar tadpole
7) finger wrist
8) advance retreat
9) vegetable fruit
10) mined parts
11) joint limb
12) bird fish
13) pitch court
14) old new
15) wood material
16) dog cat
17) eight buoy
18) drive ride
19) straw fork
20) man lady

Exercise 21: 3

1) moving static
2) herb spice
3) coop hive
4) abandon stay
5) manor signet
6) leaf bean
7) balaclava mitten
8) gaggle herd
9) cake biscuit
10) drawer rennet

PROGRESS CHARTS

Exercise	Score	Total Score	%
11: 1			
11: 2			
11: 3			
12: 1			
12: 2			
12: 3			
13: 1			
13: 2			
13: 3			
14: 1			
14: 2			
14: 3			
15: 1			
15: 2			
15: 3			
16: 1			
16: 2			
16: 3			

Exercise	Score	Total Score	%
17: 1			
17: 2			
17: 3			
18: 1			
18: 2			
18: 3			
19: 1			
19: 2			
19: 3			
20: 1			
20: 2			
20: 3			
21: 1			
21: 2			
21: 3			

Overall Score	Overall Percentage
	%

CERTIFICATE OF

ACHIEVEMENT

This certifies

____

has successfully completed

11+ Verbal Activity

Year 5–7

WORKBOOK **5**

Overall percentage score achieved [ ] %

Comment ______________________________

____

Signed ______________________________

(teacher/parent/guardian)

Date ______________________________